Founding Editor: John Milne

The Macmillan Readers provide a choice of enjoyable reading materials for learners of English. The series is published at six levels – Starter, Beginner, Elementary, Pre-intermediate, Intermediate and Upper.

Level Control
Information, structure and vocabulary are controlled to suit the students' ability at each level.

The number of words at each level:

Starter	about 300 basic words
Beginner	about 600 basic words
Elementary	about 1100 basic words
Pre-intermediate	about 1400 basic words
Intermediate	about 1600 basic words
Upper	about 2200 basic words

Vocabulary
Some difficult words and phrases in this book are important for understanding the story. Some of these words are explained in the story, some are shown in the pictures and others are marked with a number like this: ...3. Phrases are marked with P. Words with a number are explained in the *Glossary* at the end of the book and phrases are explained on the *Useful Phrases* page.

Answer Keys
Answer Keys for the *Points for Understanding* and *Exercises* sections can be found at www.macmillanenglish.com/readers.

Audio Download
There is an audio download available to buy for this title. Visit www.macmillanenglish.com/readers for more information.

Contents

	A Note About Owl Hall	4
	The People In This Story	5
1	Arrival	6
2	Exploring	11
3	Feeling Awkward	15
4	Spy Catching	21
5	The Bedroom	25
6	Something Bad	30
7	A Noise in the Night	35
8	Keep Out!	40
9	Missing Martin	44
10	An Important Discovery	48
11	Kara's Story	52
12	A New Beginning	57
13	Chapter Thirteen	66
	Points for Understanding	67
	Glossary	70
	Useful Phrases	77
	Exercises	78

A Note About Owl Hall

Owl Hall is the story of Kara and her family, and their visit to Owl Hall, a lonely, old farmhouse, which is somewhere in the British countryside. Kara is far away from everyone she knows and she only has her younger brother, Martin, to talk to. So she writes a blog on the *Owl Hall* website.

As you are reading the story, you will sometimes see this icon:

www.macmillanenglish.com/owlhall

This means that you can visit the *Owl Hall* website as well! You will find extra things to read, watch and do on the *Owl Hall* website. You can learn more about the characters and about Owl Hall itself. You can watch Kara's video and read the blog that she writes in the story. Finally, you can write about *Owl Hall* on the website, by commenting on Kara's blog. What do you think of the story? Which characters do you like best? Would you like to stay at Owl Hall?

The story of Kara and Owl Hall is not just in this book, it is on the website and also in your head. And the story does not end when you finish reading the book. That is just the beginning! What do you think happens next, in Chapter Thirteen? You can write your own ending to *Owl Hall*.

The People In This Story

Kara

Martin

Mum

The boy

Howard

1

Arrival

Kara leant her head against the car window and looked out at the other cars driving past on the motorway. Where had the cars been? Where were they going? Who were the people sitting inside them and what were they thinking?

Sometimes Mum passed the cars in front and Kara had time to look inside. Kara smiled at a man and woman having an argument in a black Ford. They were probably arguing about something stupid. It's strange, Kara thought. People always argue about things that are not important and then they don't talk about the things that *are* important. Why?

Then Mum drove faster and suddenly the man and woman were gone.

In the next car they passed, a couple were sitting in the front. They were not talking but they looked relaxed and happy together. Maybe they were listening to the radio. A young girl and boy were sitting in the back seat. The girl was asleep and the boy was playing a video game. They looked like a happy family, Kara thought. They were probably going home after a day at the beach or a visit to a castle.

Kara had started thinking about her own dad when Mum said, 'We won't be on the motorway much longer.'

'Is it far?' Martin asked, yawning[1] in the back seat.

Kara turned and looked into Martin's open mouth. She felt like she could see all the way down his throat to his stomach. It did not look very nice.

Kara looked at Mum. 'Why can't we go on a *real* holiday?' she asked.

'This *is* a real holiday,' Mum replied. 'You'll love it.'

Kara did not know where they were going for their holiday.

It was Mum's surprise. Five days ago she had suddenly decided they were going away for a week. Kara had imagined[2] lying on a beach in Spain, dancing in the streets of Rio, shopping in New York. But when they drove past the airport, she realized[3] that Mum had a different plan. Her mum's idea of a holiday was probably a week inside a caravan[4] in a wet field outside a sad seaside town.

Kara's disappointment grew when they left the motorway and drove further into the countryside. They passed through a small town and some villages, but soon there were only fields around them and there were no other cars on the road. Then Mum stopped the car.

'Are we there?' Martin asked. 'I'm hungry.'

Kara looked out of the window but it was getting dark now and she could not see much. Mum took a map from under the seat and tried to find where they were.

'We're lost, aren't we?' Kara said.

'Not *very* lost,' Mum replied. But Kara did not believe her.

'Why don't you use your phone?' Kara said.

Mum smiled at Kara. 'Good idea,' Mum said. But as she took her phone from her bag her expression[5] changed. 'Oh,' she said. 'There's no signal[6].'

'I don't believe it!' Kara cried. Then she took out her own phone to check. Mum was right. They were miles from the nearest village and they could not phone anyone for help.

Suddenly Martin kicked[7] the back of Kara's seat. Kara turned and gave her brother one of her *I'm-going-to-kill-you* looks. Martin smiled at his sister at the same time as Mum started the car.

'Let's go on,' Mum said. 'I'm sure we'll find a road sign or a house … or a phone box.'

They drove slowly down the narrow[8] country roads. For a few miles the car's headlights lit up[9] the trees on both sides of the road. Then suddenly the trees disappeared and all they could see was the road in front of them. It seemed to go on for miles and miles.

After twenty minutes they came to a crossroads[10]. Mum stopped the car and Kara looked for a road sign but she could not see one.

'There *must* be a sign,' Mum said nervously.

'Maybe it fell over,' said Kara. 'I'll look.'

Kara was pulling the car door handle[11] when suddenly the face of a large brown dog appeared at the window. It was showing its teeth and barking and growling[12]. Its eyes were staring[13] wildly at Kara and there was a red light flashing[14] on its collar[15]. Kara quickly let go of the handle and felt her mum's arms around her.

'Max!' shouted a voice from the darkness and a few seconds later a large man appeared. He pulled the dog away from the

car and looked in through the window. Then he said something that Kara could not hear.

Kara looked at her mum for permission to open the window. Mum nodded and Kara opened it a little. The man leant down so he was close to Kara.

'Don't worry – the dog won't hurt[16] you,' the man said. 'Max loves people.'

Kara looked at the dog running in circles around the car, the red light flashing on his collar, and then she looked back at the man. He was about forty years old with black hair. He wore a black jacket and when he smiled Kara could see his perfect teeth. They were *too* perfect, she thought. Kara did not like the man with the perfect teeth.

'Are you lost?' the man asked.

'Yes, we are,' Mum replied. 'We're looking for –'

'Owl Hall?' the man said.

'That's right. How did you know?' asked Mum.

'It's the only place around here …' the man replied. 'Apart from my house, of course. I'm Howard, by the way[P].'

Kara noticed that Mum seemed to relax when she heard the man's name. 'Hello, Howard. Nice to meet you,' she said.

'There was a sign here once,' said the man, pointing up the road, 'but it fell down in the storms last year. Go straight ahead and after 800 metres you'll see a turning to the left. Go down the road and you'll come to Owl Hall. Enjoy your stay.'

Mum thanked the man and they drove on. Kara looked back and watched him disappearing into the darkness. Soon the only thing she could see was the flashing red light on the dog's collar.

'There it is!' Mum said suddenly.

The car turned left and they drove down a bumpy[17] track[18], waking Martin up.

'Where are we?' Martin asked sleepily.

'We're here,' Mum said, looking at the wooden sign that hung next to a large metal gate. There was a picture of an owl on the sign and the name: 'Owl Hall'.

Mum smiled and turned to Kara. 'Please can you open the gate for me, darling?' she said.

'Why me?' Kara said as she got out of the car, closing the door loudly behind her. It was cold outside and very quiet. Kara looked around her but she could not see far in the darkness. As she walked towards the gate she heard an owl calling and the noise of something moving in the bushes[19]. Suddenly Kara thought she could feel someone or something watching her. 'It must be the owl,' she told herself as she reached the gate. Through the gate she could see the shapes of several small buildings and one large building. They had arrived but Kara did not know where they were. She only knew two things: the place was called Owl Hall and something did not feel right.

The gate creaked[20] loudly as Kara pushed it open. Then she turned and waved[21] to Mum in the car. Mum drove through the gate with Martin smiling in the back seat, and parked in the driveway[22] next to two other cars. As Kara was closing the gate, she thought she heard a voice whispering in her ear.

'Kara! Help me. Let me go!' the voice said.

But when Kara turned round, no one was there.

2

Exploring[23]

'So? What do you think?' Mum asked Kara.

Owl Hall was a large farmhouse building which surrounded[24] a central courtyard[25]. The house had lots of windows but there were no lights on and inside it was very dark. There was just one security[26] light in the courtyard. In the centre of the courtyard there was a round pond[27] which had a strange silver sphere[28] in its middle. The first word Kara thought of when she saw Owl Hall was 'spooky[29]' but she did not want to upset her mother so she said, 'Wow!'

Martin knew what Kara was thinking and he started laughing. Kara put a finger to her mouth – she was telling him to be quiet. Then she saw a security camera looking at them.

'They told me the keys were under the owl on the left,' Mum said, reaching down. She lifted a stone owl next to the front door and found a set of keys underneath it. Then she unlocked the door and they went into the main house. The entrance hall was quite small with a cupboard and a table. Above the table there was a photograph of Owl Hall. On the left there was a staircase going up to the next floor and next to the staircase there was a door. There was another door to the right of the table.

'Look!' said Mum. 'Here's a plan of the house.' She picked up the plan and a Welcome Pack[30] from the table. She studied the plan for a moment and then pointed at the door next to the staircase. 'This must be the kitchen,' she said.

She opened the door and they walked into a large kitchen. Kara had expected an old house to be full of old things but the kitchen was all new. On the right there was a big cooker, some cupboards, a sink and a dishwasher. There were more cupboards on the left and a fridge with alphabet letters stuck to it. At the end of the room there was a large window and a rectangular table with six chairs around it.

'What an amazing kitchen,' Mum said.

'Where are we?' asked Kara.

'Owl Hall,' said Mum. 'I told you.'

Kara sat at the table and opened the Welcome Pack. A letter welcomed them to Owl Hall.

Dear guests,

We hope you enjoy your stay at Owl Hall, the perfect place to escape from the stress of everyday life. Owl Hall has four holiday homes. Apart from the main house there are three smaller cottages[31]. All our guests can use the gym and games areas in the main house. You are welcome to explore the grounds, which include a wood and a small lake[32] where you can swim in summer. While you are here, we hope you will keep a record of your stay on our own private blog.

Best wishes,
The Owl Hall team

Martin sat down next to Kara and stared at her. 'Kara, I'm bored. Can we go and explore the house?' he said.

Kara looked across at Mum, who was searching in the cupboards. 'Can we explore, Mum?' she asked.

'I can't but you can,' replied Mum. 'I'll need to make us something to eat. Don't go too far. And don't go outside. It's too late.'

So Kara and Martin ran from the kitchen and went upstairs. At the top of the stairs there was a bathroom on the right and a large bedroom with a double bed. To the left there was a corridor[33] with a smaller bedroom, a bathroom and another bedroom. They went down the corridor. Martin jumped onto the bed in the last bedroom.

12

'This is my room!' he shouted to Kara. 'You can have the other one.'

Kara looked around the room. Its white walls were bare – they had no pictures on them. There was a bed, a chair and a table with a light on it. And that was all.

'It's like a prison cell[34],' she said.

'I know,' Martin laughed. 'That's why I like it.'

'Don't talk rubbish, Martin,' said Kara. Then she took out her phone and saw there was still no signal.

'I can't believe it!' she said. 'We're cut off[35] from the world.'

'I think I saw a laptop in your room,' Martin said. 'Maybe you can use the Internet.'

So Kara went into the other small bedroom. Her room was much nicer than Martin's. There were shelves with lots of books. The walls were sky blue, which was her favourite colour, and there were pictures on the walls. One of the pictures was a copy of her favourite painting – *The Bedroom* by Vincent van Gogh.

Martin was right. There was a laptop on the desk. She turned on the computer and waited. A few seconds later a dark Owl Hall 'Welcome' page appeared with the message:

`Welcome to Owl Hall. Click`[36]` here to start.`

Kara tried to log on[37] to the Internet, but it was impossible to close the Owl Hall page.

'Spooky.' Martin was looking over her shoulder. 'We're in prison in Owl Hall.'

Kara clicked on the link to enter the Owl Hall site and a new page opened. There were three links on the page:

`Explore Owl Hall`
`Blog`
`About Owl Hall`

www.macmillanenglish.com/owlhall

She chose the third link.

'I want to know where we are,' she explained to Martin.

But there was no address and no map on the 'About Owl Hall' page. The page showed the same information she had read in the Welcome Pack. 'Owl Hall has four holiday homes. Apart from the main house there are three smaller cottages. All our guests …'

'Well, I can't find out where we are but I can write a blog,' she said.

Kara was opening the 'Blog' page when she heard her mother's voice calling from the bottom of the stairs.

'Dinner's ready!' Mum called.

'Coming!' shouted Kara.

Kara was shutting down the laptop when she heard Martin close the bedroom door.

'What are you doing, Martin?' she asked.

'Kara,' he said, sounding nervous. 'Can I talk to you?'

'Of course you can, Martin,' she replied. 'What do you want to talk about?'

Martin sat down on the bed and looked at his hands. 'Something's not right,' he said. 'I … don't know how to say it.'

'It's OK, Martin. I'm listening,' Kara said.

Then Martin started biting his fingernails[38]. 'It's this place … this holiday. I've got a bad feeling, Kara. Please don't laugh,' he said nervously.

But Kara was not laughing. She waited for Martin to go on. Sometimes it was important to give Martin time to think.

'I think someone is watching us,' he said.

Kara did not say anything because she had felt the same thing. From the moment they had walked into the courtyard, she had felt someone watching her. She remembered the security camera and the voice that whispered to her. 'Kara!' the voice had said. 'Help me. Let me go!'

'I think I saw someone in the courtyard …' said Martin. 'It

was while you were using the computer. You won't let them take me away, will you, Kara?' he went on. 'Please promise you won't leave me.'

'I won't leave you,' said Kara. Then she reached out and held Martin's hand.

3

Feeling Awkward[39]

Nobody said much at dinner. When Martin finished eating, he got up silently and went into the living room. After he had left, Mum put her fork down and looked at her daughter.

'Why was your bedroom door shut earlier?' she asked.

'I'm allowed some privacy[40], aren't I?' replied Kara angrily.

'Of course you are. But ...'

'But *what?*' said Kara. 'Are you worried I'm going to do something stupid again?'

'No, of course not,' said Mum. There was an awkward silence.

That's a funny word, Kara thought suddenly. 'Awkward'. It sounds ... awkward. It looks ... awkward. Kara looked across at the alphabet letters that were stuck to the fridge. She imagined the letters of the word moving *awkwardly* on the fridge door, changing position, spelling the word 'awkward'. Then she imagined four of the letters from the word moved again. This time they spelt her name.

'Kara.' Martin was calling her from the living room. 'Kara, there's no TV!'

Kara stared angrily at her mother. 'Mum,' she said, 'is there really no TV?'

'I wanted to find somewhere quiet to go on holiday,' replied Mum. 'Somewhere we could spend some time together.'

Kara left the kitchen, still angry, and went through to the living room. It was a long room with large leather armchairs and sofas grouped around a fireplace.

'What are you doing, Martin?' Kara asked.

Martin was kneeling down[41] and putting pieces of newspaper in the fireplace. His eyes were bright with excitement.

'Look, Kara! I'm making a fire,' he said. 'Come and help me.'

'I don't think we should make a fire, Martin,' Kara replied. 'Mum will be very angry.'

But Martin wasn't listening. He was concentrating on building his fire. He put more pieces of newspaper in the fireplace and then took a box of matches[42] from a small table.

'Are you ready, Kara?' he said.

Then Martin took a match from the box and lit it.

'Martin! Don't!' Kara shouted.

16

She ran to the fireplace and took the match from Martin's hand before he could light the fire. Mum heard Kara shouting and she came quickly from the kitchen.

'What's going on?' Mum asked.

'She started it!' Martin shouted, pointing at Kara.

'It was Martin!' Kara said.

Mum looked at Kara. 'You're tired, Kara. Go to bed,' she said calmly.

'But Mum –' said Kara.

'I said – go to bed!' said Mum.

Kara walked out of the room and quickly went upstairs and into her bedroom, closing the door behind her. She stood next to the door and listened. For a few minutes she could not hear anything. Then she heard Martin running up the stairs and down the corridor. He went past Kara's door and straight into his own room. After that, there was silence.

Kara sat down at the desk and turned on the laptop. She logged on to the Owl Hall site and clicked on the 'Blog' section. A message invited her to start a blog and keep a record of her stay. At the top of the page there was a title: 'Day 1'. She stared at the words for about a minute, thinking about what to write. Then suddenly the words rushed[43] into her head.

 www.macmillanenglish.com/owlhall

When Kara went downstairs for breakfast the next morning, Mum was sitting at the table reading a magazine. Kara drank some fruit juice and watched her mother.

When Mum had first talked about this holiday, Kara thought that she wanted to talk about 'the incident[44]'. Mum did not want to talk about it at home so Kara thought her plan had been to take Kara and Martin away to a place where talking would be easier. Kara hoped there would be long conversations about what had happened and how they could help each other. But now Kara was not so sure. Mum and Kara were alone[45] in the kitchen and it was the perfect moment to start talking. Mum did not seem to want to talk about 'the incident'. She wanted to talk about the weather, about how well she had slept and about breakfast cereals. Mum did not like talking about problems. Dad had been the opposite. Dad always said that a problem could not be fixed until everyone sat down and talked about it. Then they could find a solution[46] that they were all happy with. But Mum did not agree with him and she did not want to sit down and talk. There had been a lot of arguments before Dad left to go to Australia.

'Can I go out?' Kara asked.

'Alright but don't go too far,' Mum replied.

Martin was in the bathroom having a shower. Kara knocked on the door and told him she was going to explore outside. He said he would come out in a minute. Then Kara put on a jacket and picked up her phone. There was still no signal but as she was looking at the phone Kara had an idea. She could use its camera to make a video of Owl Hall. She turned the phone onto video and started filming as she walked out of her room and along the corridor towards the stairs.

'Awkward Productions presents ...' she said in her worst American accent, 'Owl Hall – the movie ... directed by Kara.' She imagined herself making a real film as she moved the phone around her, exploring the floor, the walls, the doors. 'This is Mum's bedroom. She has the biggest bedroom, of course ... and now we're going downstairs and out the front door ... into the courtyard of Owl Hall.' Kara filmed the courtyard and the pond with the strange silver sphere in the middle. Through the windows on one side of the courtyard she could see the gym that she had read about in the Welcome Pack.

Kara's video tour continued outside the courtyard in the driveway. She filmed the Owl Hall sign they had seen in the darkness when they had arrived the night before. Then she walked to the far end of the building and filmed two of the holiday cottages next to the main house. The cottages looked empty. After that she walked to the other side of the house, past the window of the third small cottage. She looked in the window but could not see anything. Behind the main building there was a large, open field with trees at the end. Kara held her phone camera up to film the trees. She wanted to record the sound of the leaves moving in the wind.

'And over there,' she said, 'there's a ...'

Kara moved the phone camera towards where some trees and bushes were hiding a large old barn[47]. As Kara began to film the barn, she thought she saw someone moving in the bushes. But as she was going to get a closer look, Martin suddenly appeared and jumped on her. He pulled her to the ground and knocked the phone from her hand. Kara pulled herself free and looked over at the barn just in time[P] to see a figure[48] running into the trees at the end of the field.

'What is it, Kara?' said Martin, laughing. 'Why do you look so frightened? Have you seen a ghost?'

'What is it, Kara?' said Martin, laughing.
'Why do you look so frightened? Have you seen a ghost?'

4

Spy[49] Catching

'Where are we going?' Kara asked. She was following Martin down the bumpy track that passed Owl Hall.

'I want to see where this track goes,' Martin answered.

After a hundred metres, the track started to go up a hill. Kara heard her mother's voice inside her head saying, 'Don't go too far'. Kara used the phone to film the ground beneath her feet, the bushes on either side of the track and the fields behind the bushes. Martin walked along the track in front of her. He was carrying a large stick[50] he had found in the bushes. Kara watched him lift the stick and hit a bush.

A brother and sister can be so different, she thought. She and Martin looked very different. Kara had dark hair while Martin had ginger[51] hair. Kara had green eyes while Martin had brown eyes. Kara was quite tall and slim[52] but Martin was shorter and well-built[53]. Martin was strong and Kara was not. Sometimes, when they fought, Kara thought he did not know how strong he really was. But probably the biggest difference between them was their personalities. Kara was quiet and shy while Martin was loud and outgoing[54]. In many ways, Martin was like his father and Kara was like her mother.

When Mum and Dad had decided to separate[55], Martin had changed. It was not a sudden change. Kara was not sure if Mum had noticed the change at first. Kara had noticed it because she spent a lot of time with her brother. In the past, Kara had usually known what Martin was going to say or do. During the separation, it became difficult to know what Martin was thinking. His character would sometimes suddenly change. When Martin's character changed, Kara had to watch him carefully.

They were quite far away from Owl Hall now and Kara was starting to worry.

'I think we should go back,' she said.

'No, there's a house up that hill. I want to see it,' said Martin.

So they climbed the hill and reached the house. There they came face to face[P] with Max, the dog from last night. Kara and Martin did not move. Kara remembered Howard, the dog's owner. He had said that the dog liked people but Kara thought it looked dangerous.

'Max!' Martin said to the dog. 'It's OK. We're friends.'

Then Martin walked over to the dog and stroked[56] its head. The dog wagged[57] its tail.

'He's OK,' Martin said. 'He's big but he won't hurt you.'

They walked through the gate and came to the house. It was a tall, narrow building that did not look loved.

'This must be Howard's house,' Kara said. 'He said he had a house near Owl Hall.'

Suddenly a face appeared at one of the upstairs windows.

'Come on!' Martin shouted as he turned and ran back down the track in the direction of Owl Hall. Kara ran after him, imagining the person at the window running downstairs and chasing them.

––––––––

When they were back in her bedroom at Owl Hall, Kara and Martin connected the phone to the laptop and watched the video that Kara had made earlier.

'Awkward Productions presents …' Kara's voice said. Kara did not want to watch the whole video. She wanted to find the moment when she had seen someone or something in the bushes outside the barn.

'This is it!' Kara said when she reached the moment when the phone fell to the ground. She went back a few seconds and watched carefully. As the image moved in closer to the barn, she pressed *pause* and pointed to a shape in the bushes.

'Look, Martin. Can you see?' she asked. 'There's someone watching us.'

Martin nodded his head and watched the shape moving in the bushes. A few seconds later the phone fell to the ground.

'It's a spy,' Martin told her.

'I'm going to upload the video to my blog,' Kara replied.

She logged in to the site and started uploading the video. Suddenly a message appeared on the screen. It said:

You have one new message. Click here to read.

Kara looked at Martin, who nodded.

'Go on,' he said.

She clicked on the link and a new window opened with a message.

I need to talk to you. Meet me in the barn at five o'clock. Come alone. A friend.

'It's a message from the spy,' Martin said. 'Be careful. It might be a trap[58].'

'Don't be stupid,' replied Kara.

Then both of them jumped because someone had rung the doorbell. Kara and Martin waited for Mum to answer the door but a few seconds later the bell rang again. Then the visitor started knocking on the front door.

'I'll go,' said Kara. She looked from Martin to the laptop. 'Don't read my blog, Martin.'

'Why would I want to read your blog?' Martin asked.

Kara walked quickly downstairs and opened the front door. The man they had met last night was standing outside. He smiled, showing his perfect teeth, and held out his hand.

'Hello,' he said. 'I'm Howard. Do you remember me?'

'I remember,' said Kara, but she did not shake his hand. She was wondering if Howard had watched her and Martin when they had visited the narrow house on the hill.

'Is your mother at home?' Howard asked.

'I think so,' Kara replied.

Kara did not ask the man to come inside. She went through to the kitchen but her mother was not there. Kara looked in the living room but she was not there either. Then she went back into the kitchen and through the utility room[59] to the gym. There she found Mum jogging on a treadmill[60].

'Mum!' Kara said. 'We've got a visitor.'

Mum looked up. But she was not looking at Kara. She was looking over her shoulder. Kara turned round and saw Howard in the doorway.

'Howard!' Mum said, as if she was speaking to an old friend. 'What are you doing here?'

'I wanted to see how you are,' Howard replied.

'We're fine,' Mum said. She stopped the treadmill and Kara noticed that she seemed nervous.

'Kara, darling …' Mum said. She usually called Kara *darling* when she wanted her to do something. 'Please can you go and make some tea? Would you like some tea, Howard?'

'I'd love some,' he said, turning and smiling at Kara.

Kara knew that neither Howard nor Mum really wanted a cup of tea. They wanted Kara to leave them alone so they could talk. As Kara walked back to the kitchen she heard the door closing quietly behind her. She searched round the kitchen and managed to make two cups of tea.

'Tea's ready!' she shouted.

Then she went back upstairs to her room and decided to play the video again. She stared for a long time at the person in the bushes, wondering who 'a friend' might be.

 **www.macmillanenglish.com/owlhall**

5

The Bedroom

Vincent van Gogh painted *The Bedroom* in 1888. Kara knew this because she had written about the painting for a school project. Her Art teacher, Mr Howlett, had asked the class to write about a picture that meant something special to them.

Kara had fallen in love with *The Bedroom* from the moment she first saw it in a book at school. It was a very simple picture of the artist's bedroom in the Yellow House, in a town called Arles in France. The bedroom in the painting was a strange shape. One of the things Kara liked about the painting was the colours. The walls and doors were pale blue. The wooden bed and the chairs were butter yellow and the windows were green. The colours made Kara think of the sun. She could see herself in the room, looking out of the windows onto the streets of a sleepy French town. She had always wanted a bedroom like the one in *The Bedroom*.

How strange, she thought, to find my favourite picture here.

Suddenly Martin ran into the room and jumped onto the bed. 'Come on, Kara. It's time to go and meet the spy!' he shouted.

'*You* can't come with me,' she replied. 'He said I had to go alone.'

'*He?*' said Martin, looking upset. 'How do you know the spy is a *he?* Anyway, I'm not going to let you go on your own. I'm coming and that's final.'

So Kara and Martin left the house together. They crossed the courtyard and walked past the cottages to the barn behind the bushes. The barn was old and looked as if it might fall down at any moment. Kara walked in first, followed by Martin.

She had expected the barn to be empty but it was full of old furniture, paintings, boxes, broken computers and a hundred other strange things.

'This place is amazing,' Martin said, sitting down on an old blue armchair.

'What time is it?' asked Kara.

Martin looked across at an old clock in the corner. 'Ten past five,' he said. 'The spy is late.'

They waited until half past five but nobody came. Kara felt disappointed. She had been excited at the idea of finding a new friend. Martin, however, seemed happy.

'Come on,' he said. 'Let's go back.'

Martin started walking back towards the house. Kara waited until he had left and then looked around the barn one last time. 'Hello? Are you here?' she called, hoping the person was hiding in the shadows. But there was no answer. All she could hear was the sound of the clock.

As she followed Martin back to the house it started to rain lightly. Kara looked up and saw dark clouds in the sky above her so she started walking more quickly down the path. As she passed the cottages, she thought she saw a curtain move inside one of the windows. She thought about knocking on the cottage door but now the rain was falling more heavily so she went on back to the house.

When she got back, Mum was in the kitchen preparing dinner. There was no sign of Howard. Kara was glad.

'Mum?' she asked. 'Are there other people staying here? I mean, in the other buildings?'

'I don't know,' replied Mum. 'I don't think so. Howard didn't say anything.'

'Howard? Why would he know?' Kara asked.

Her mother's face went a little red. 'He lives up the road,' she said, 'so he knows who comes and who goes.'

'Have you met him before?' Kara asked.

'Howard? No, of course not,' Mum answered quickly. 'Why do you ask?'

'No reason,' Kara replied. 'I was just curious[61].'

There was something strange about Howard and about the way Mum acted when she was with him. When they had been lost in the car, Mum seemed to relax when Howard had told her his name. There had also been something strange about the way Mum had looked at him in the gym. Had they met before? Or was she attracted[62] to him? Kara hoped not. She hoped her mother was not in love with Howard. The idea made her feel ill.

'How long until dinner, Mum?' Kara asked.

'Five minutes,' replied her mother.

So Kara went to look for Martin. She found him in the games room.

'This is cool,' Martin said. He was throwing darts[63] at a dartboard.

A large pool[64] table dominated the room. Apart from the pool table, there was a small round table, the dartboard, and a big bookcase full of books and board games.

'Do you want to play?' Martin asked as he walked to the dartboard and pulled out the darts he had just thrown. Kara shook her head.

'I've been thinking,' Martin said, 'about the spy. I think I need to teach him something.'

'Teach him?' said Kara.

She watched Martin throw more darts at the dartboard.

'What do you mean?'

'I want to teach him that it's bad to spy on other people,' Martin replied. 'After dinner I'm going to go spy hunting[65]. Do you want to come?'

'No, I don't,' she said. 'You won't hurt him, will you?'

'Bullseye!' Martin shouted as a dart hit the very centre of the dartboard.

After dinner, while Martin was spy hunting, Kara turned on the laptop and wrote a message to her mystery 'friend'.

`Please be careful,` she wrote. `Martin is looking for you.`

She pressed *send* and quickly received a reply.

`Thanks for the warning`[66], read the message.

`Who are you?` Kara wrote back. `Why didn't you come to the barn?`

There was a pause. Then the reply came.

`I told you before. I'm a friend. I went to the barn but you weren't alone. I heard you talking to someone. I asked you to come alone.`

`I was with Martin. He's my brother,` Kara typed. Pause.

`I have to see you alone,` the message came back. `How about tomorrow morning, at eight o'clock?`

`I'll be there,` Kara wrote.

And the message came back: `I must go now.`

Then Kara typed quickly. `Wait! Tell me your name.`

Pause.

Kara waited for an answer but none came. Had Martin found her 'friend'? What had happened?

Later, when Kara finally heard her brother's footsteps coming along the corridor, she opened the door and called out to him. 'Martin! What happened?'

Martin turned and looked back at her. His face and hair were wet from the rain.

'Did you find him?' Kara asked.

Martin smiled. 'He managed to escape,' he said. '*Someone* must have warned him.'

'It wasn't me,' Kara replied, too quickly.

Kara watched as the smile disappeared from Martin's face. She felt uncomfortable because she had lied to her brother and he knew she had lied. What was happening? She had never lied to him before. Martin waited for Kara to say something but she was silent. Then Martin turned and walked to his room.

'Goodnight, Kara,' he said, closing his bedroom door behind him.

6

Something Bad

Kara woke up early the next morning. She got dressed quickly and then quietly opened the bedroom door. She checked that the door to Martin's room was shut, then she walked slowly down the corridor to the top of the stairs. She waited a few seconds and listened. Was Mum awake? When she was sure that no one had heard her, she went downstairs and silently opened the front door.

Outside it was a beautiful fresh morning. Yesterday's rain had washed everything clean and the leaves on the trees were a deep green. Kara breathed in the clean country air as she walked quickly past the cottages towards the barn.

Inside the barn everything was quiet. All she could hear was the old clock and some birds in the roof. Kara looked around her.

'Hello? Are you there?' she said. There was no reply so she walked through to the other end of the barn. There were several large pieces of furniture along the back wall, including cupboards and wardrobes. A large mirror was leaning against one of the wardrobes. Kara stood in front of the mirror and looked at her reflection[67].

'Hello,' she said to her reflection.

Suddenly she realized that there was another person's reflection standing next to hers in the mirror.

'Hello,' the reflection said.

Kara looked at the face in the mirror. It was the face of a boy about the same age and height as her. He was quite thin and his face was pale. His hair was brown and wavy, and he had large brown eyes. He was holding a red book. Kara turned round to look at the boy beside her but there was no one there.

*Suddenly she realized that there was another person's
reflection standing next to hers in the mirror.*

— 'Where are you?' Kara said.

There was a silence. Then she heard a voice shout, 'Over here!'

And the boy appeared again from behind a bookcase. 'Welcome to my home,' he said.

'Your *home*? Do you live here alone in the barn?' Kara asked.

The boy looked around him. 'Not really. I'm staying in the smallest cottage. But I like it here. People don't come here.'

'Don't you like people?' Kara asked, but the boy did not answer and he looked at her in a strange way. Kara thought that maybe he could see what she was thinking. She felt embarrassed[68] and looked away.

'What's your name?' she asked.

But again the boy did not answer.

'My name's –' Kara began.

'Kara,' the boy said. 'I know. It's a nice name.' Then he smiled. He had a very friendly smile.

'In your message,' Kara went on, 'you said that you needed to talk to me. Why?'

The boy's expression changed. He looked very serious.

'Do you remember that you heard a voice ... when you arrived at Owl Hall?' he said.

'Yes, I remember,' said Kara. 'Was it *your* voice?'

The boy shook his head. Kara did not understand. How did the boy know that she had heard a voice? She had not told anyone. Then she realized that the boy must have read her blog.

'What did the voice say?' the boy asked.

Kara wanted to tell the boy about the voice but something was stopping her. She did not know the boy so how could she trust him? He did not trust her. He had not even told her his name. But there was something about[P] him that made Kara feel safe. She wanted him to be her friend. At that moment she wanted a friend more than anything in the world. So she decided to trust him and tell him what the voice had said. But as she was about to speak, she heard a different voice behind her.

'Don't tell him, Kara.' Martin had followed her into the barn. 'What do you want?' Martin said to the boy. He walked over and stood next to his sister. 'Leave Kara alone[P].'

'What's wrong?' the boy asked Kara. He did not look at Martin. 'Is it your brother? Tell him to go and leave us alone.'

Martin laughed and took hold of Kara's hand. He held it tightly as he spoke to the boy. Kara began to feel very nervous. When her brother became angry she did not know what he would do next.

'I'm not going anywhere,' Martin said to the boy. 'I think *you* should go.'

Kara could feel Martin's anger growing as he pressed her hand tighter and tighter.

'Martin's right,' she whispered. 'You should go.'

There was a pause while the boy looked at her and tried to decide what he should do. And then, he walked out of the barn. Martin let go of Kara's hand.

'Did you see that?' he shouted. 'I made him go! He was scared of me!'

Martin was right. He had scared the boy away. He had scared Kara too. She started walking out of the barn and Martin ran after her.

'Where are you going?' he shouted. But Kara would not answer him.

Martin followed Kara back to the house and sat opposite her at the kitchen table. He watched her eating her breakfast cereal while Mum was preparing coffee.

'Shall we tell Mum ... about your friend the spy?' Martin whispered across the table.

'He's not a spy,' Kara replied.

'Who's not a spy?' Mum asked as she sat down at the table.

'Why can't you leave me alone?' Kara shouted at Martin. Then she got up from the table and left the room. Mum called after her.

'Kara! Where are you going?'

Kara did not answer. She wanted to get away from Martin but he was already behind her.

'Where are you going, Kara?' he said. 'Are you going to see your boyfriend?'

Kara walked up the stairs and Martin followed her.

'Last night you lied to me, Kara,' he whispered. 'Why did you do that?'

'I didn't lie to you,' she said.

'You're doing it again. Why are you lying to me?' Martin said.

'I'm not lying to you!' Kara said.

'And this morning,' Martin went on. 'You left me alone. You broke your promise[P].'

When she got to the top of the stairs, Kara turned and looked down at her brother. She was surprised to see that he was crying.

'What did I promise?' she asked.

'You promised not to leave me!' Martin shouted.

At that moment Kara had a very bad thought. She thought how easy it would be to push Martin and watch him fall down the stairs. For a few seconds she imagined him lying at the bottom, looking up at her with dead eyes. Kara was shocked. How could she think such a terrible thing? What was happening to her? She loved her brother.

Martin tried to get past Kara but she stopped him.

'I'm sorry, Martin. I promise I won't leave you,' she repeated again and again. 'I promise I won't leave you.'

———

Kara kept her promise[P] and did not leave Martin for the rest of the day. They played cards together. They read comics together.

34

They chased each other around the house and walked down the bumpy track together. Kara wanted Martin to trust her again. But all the time they were together, Kara was thinking about the boy from the barn. She was wondering where he was and what he was doing. Was he watching them?

Later that evening, after Martin had gone to bed, Kara sat at the desk in her room and wrote her blog. There was something different about this blog entry. This time she was writing her blog for someone – for the boy in the barn. She wanted him to read it. She needed to explain why she had told him to leave this morning. She wanted to tell him how much Martin needed her and how she had promised not to leave him. She did not tell him about the moment when she had thought about pushing Martin down the stairs. Kara did not feel very good when she remembered that feeling. Did she really want to kill her brother?

www.macmillanenglish.com/owlhall

7

A Noise in the Night

'What was that?' Kara asked herself as she opened her eyes. It was the middle of the night and she was lying in bed in the dark. Kara thought she had heard something but she was not sure. A minute passed and nothing happened so she yawned and closed her eyes again. I must have been dreaming, she thought. She was almost asleep when she heard the noise again. It was coming from outside and it sounded like something heavy falling and hitting the ground. What could it be?

Kara turned on the light on the bedside table and looked at the time on her phone. It was three o'clock in the morning. She got out of bed and looked out of the window but it was black outside and the only thing she could see was her reflection. Then she heard the noise again. It was coming from the direction of the barn.

Kara decided to investigate[69] so she put on some clothes and walked down the corridor to Martin's room. His bedroom door was half-open.

'Martin?' Kara said. But Martin was not there. She looked around the empty room and suddenly felt frightened. Where had he gone?

Kara thought about waking Mum but she did not want to worry her. So she went downstairs, opened the front door and walked out into the night. It was dark outside but there was a strange orange light in one corner of the sky. It was not a bright light but it shone[70] on the trees and turned them a strange colour. Kara knew immediately what the light was and where it was coming from because she had seen a light like this before. She ran as fast as she could, down the path towards the barn. As she got closer, the noise became louder and the light became brighter. The closer she got to the barn, the hotter she felt. And then suddenly she was standing in front of the barn and it was burning. The barn was on fire! Flames were pouring[71] from the doors and the roof. Kara looked in horror as parts of the roof fell down, crashing to the ground. This was the sound she had heard from her bedroom!

'Martin!' she shouted. 'Are you in there?'

But Martin did not answer. Where was he? Kara tried to get closer to the door but there was too much heat. All she could do was stand and watch the burning building.

'Martin!' she shouted again. 'What have you done?'

Suddenly Kara heard the sound of a fire alarm but it was not coming from the barn. It was coming from behind her ... from

Owl Hall. She left the barn and ran back to the house. Owl Hall was now on fire! There were flames in all the windows, lighting the courtyard. In the middle of the courtyard, Martin was sitting on the ground, watching the fire around him.

'Martin!' Kara shouted. She was trying to be heard over the noise of the alarm.

'I'm making a fire, Kara!' Martin said, his eyes bright with excitement.

'Where's Mum?' Kara asked. 'Is she still inside the house? Please say she's not inside the house.'

Martin looked at Kara and his expression quickly changed to horror. He stood up and ran into the burning house. A few seconds later he was at one of the upstairs windows, surrounded by flames. For a moment Kara thought she saw her brother hold out his hand towards her. Was he asking her to help him?

Then the roof of the building suddenly collapsed[72] and Martin disappeared.

'Martin!' Kara screamed in shock. 'Mum! No-o-o-o-o!'

Kara closed her eyes and cried out in pain. Then she felt her body moving from side to side. Someone was shaking her and she could hear a woman's voice.

'Kara!'

It was Mum's voice. Kara opened her eyes.

'Are you alright?' Mum asked.

Kara did not understand. She was in the courtyard. She looked around her at the buildings. There was no fire. The roof was still on the building. The fire alarm was silent. Everything was the same as it had been before.

Kara felt her mother's arms around her, holding her tight. She immediately felt safe again.

'You were sleepwalking[73],' Mum said. 'Are you alright?'

'I'm alright,' Kara replied. It had been a dream. A bad dream. A nightmare. It was not the first time that Kara had sleepwalked. It had happened three times since 'the incident'.

'You were sleepwalking,' Mum said. 'Are you alright?'

Back inside the house, Mum made Kara some hot chocolate and they sat at the kitchen table together. Mum watched Kara as she drank the chocolate.

'I've asked Howard to come and see us tomorrow,' her mother said.

'Oh no,' Kara said. 'He's spooky.'

'Howard is a friend so I want you to be nice to him,' Mum went on. 'Is that OK?'

For a moment Kara said nothing. Then she slowly nodded her head and went back upstairs. She went straight to Martin's room.

'Martin?' she whispered. 'Are you awake?'

'No,' Martin replied. Kara sat down on the bed. Martin was lying on his side, facing away from Kara.

'I just had a terrible dream,' she said.

'I know,' Martin replied.

'How do you know?' Kara asked, surprised.

Martin did not move. 'I was in it, remember?' he said. 'Why didn't you come into the house with me?'

Kara was confused. Had she and Martin had the same dream? She did not want to answer his question so she got up and walked out of the room. As she was closing the door, she heard Martin say, 'I held out my hand to you but you didn't come.'

Kara could still see her brother in the burning house, holding out his hand to her. She closed the door and stood in the corridor for a moment. Then she went to her room and wrote her blog. Why had she had such a terrible dream?

www.macmillanenglish.com/owlhall

8

Keep Out!^P

'Keep out!'

Kara stared at the handwritten notice on Martin's door. Her brother had terrible handwriting. Kara's handwriting was neat[74] and clear. It was another difference between them. Kara decided that one day she would make a list of all the differences between herself and Martin.

For a moment she thought of knocking on his door. She was still feeling confused about last night and she wanted to know how Martin had known about her dream. But the sign said 'Keep out' so she left him alone and went to the kitchen to have breakfast with Mum. Then she decided to go back to the barn because she wanted to make sure it was still there. She also wanted to find her new friend.

It felt strange walking into the same barn that had been burning down in her dream. This morning it looked the same as always. Kara looked around her and suddenly she saw the boy in the corner. He was sitting in the blue armchair and writing in the old book with the red cover.

'Hello,' Kara said.

The boy looked up and smiled. 'Hello,' he said. 'Are you alone?'

Kara nodded. 'Yes, I am.'

'Where's your brother?' he asked, looking around the barn.

'He's in his room.' Kara laughed. 'He wants to be alone.'

'Good,' said the boy.

'He thinks you're a spy,' said Kara. 'Are you?'

'Maybe,' the boy replied. Then he smiled and closed the book.

'What are you writing?' Kara asked.

'Nothing,' the boy replied, putting the book down on the table beside him. 'I know a place where your brother won't find us. Do you want to go there?'

Kara nodded and followed the boy out of the barn. They did not go back down the path towards the house. They walked round the side of the barn and crossed the field behind it. At the end of the field there were some trees on each side of a stream[75]. This was the first time that Kara had seen the stream and she stopped for a moment to watch the water running over the rocks and stones.

'Come on!' the boy shouted as he jumped to the other side of the water.

The stream was not very wide so Kara could easily jump across and climb up the other side. She looked behind her. Through the trees she could see the barn and Owl Hall in the distance. For a moment she thought of Martin sitting alone in his room but then she decided to stop thinking about him. She ran after the boy and soon they were walking side by side up the hill.

'Where are we going?' Kara asked.

'You'll see,' the boy said. 'It's not far.'

At the top of the hill, they came to a path that took them to a gate. On the other side of the gate there was a wood with hundreds of tall trees. The boy climbed over the gate but Kara stopped. The wood looked dark and mysterious and she was feeling a little afraid.

'What's wrong?' the boy asked.

'I don't know you,' Kara said. 'I don't even know your name.'

The boy looked disappointed. 'What's so important about a name?' he asked. 'Would you trust me more if you knew it?'

It was strange, but Kara felt that she could trust the boy. She did not know why, but she felt that they had something in common[P]. She had always been taught not to trust strangers and it was a rule she followed. But was the boy a stranger? Not really. He was staying at Owl Hall too. So Kara decided to climb the gate and follow him into the wood.

They walked quickly between the trees. It was much darker in the wood. Sometimes the sunlight passed between the trees and lit up the ground beneath them.

'Come on!' the boy shouted and he started running.

Kara ran after him and then suddenly they were coming out on the other side of the trees, back into the daylight.

'Wow!' Kara said.

They were standing at the top of a hill looking down at a lake. The water in the lake was calm, reflecting the sky above it. There were hills all around the lake which hid it from the outside world.

'Wow!' Kara said again. 'It's amazing.'

'I know where there's a boat,' said the boy. 'Come on. I'll take you to the island.'

Kara followed the boy down the hill. There were some bushes by the lake and hidden in the bushes there was a rowing boat[76], lying upside down[77].

'Help me turn it over,' the boy said.

They turned the boat over and pulled it into the water. Then the boy went into the bushes and came back with two oars. Kara got into the boat first and the boy followed her. He sat down in the middle of the boat, put the oars in position and started rowing. Kara sat at the back of the boat and looked down into the water. It looked dark and deep. She put her hand in the water and it felt cool and fresh.

They did not speak for the rest of the journey. The boy rowed while Kara looked up at the sky. She felt as calm as the water in the lake. She felt good – very good.

The island was near the other side of the lake. It was smaller than Kara had expected. There was just enough space for a few trees, for the boat, and for Kara and the boy.

After they had pulled the boat onto the island, they sat down on the ground and stared across the water.

'How did you find this place?' Kara asked.

'Last week when I was out walking I found the boat and rowed it here,' the boy said. 'Now I come here every day. It's my island.'

'You're strange!' Kara laughed.

'You are too,' said the boy.

They sat in silence for a while and then the boy looked at Kara.

'Do you ever feel like someone or something is chasing you?' he said.

'No,' Kara said, too quickly.

The boy stood up and started throwing stones into the water. 'I do,' he said.

'Why are they chasing you?' Kara asked.

'Because I'm different,' he replied.

Kara got up and stood beside the boy. He threw a stone into the lake and they watched it bounce[78] across the water several times before it sank[79].

'We're all different,' she said. 'Everyone in the world is different.'

'No, they're not,' he said. 'Everyone else is the same or trying to be the same. But you and me, we're different. That's why we're here.'

'On the island?' Kara asked.

'No, stupid.' The boy looked into Kara's eyes. 'That's why we're at Owl Hall.'

9

Missing Martin

When Kara got back to Owl Hall it was the afternoon and the 'Keep out' sign was still on Martin's door. Kara knocked on it but there was no answer. She did not care. Her head was full of a thousand other things and she wanted to write them all down. She went to her room and started writing her blog but it was difficult to express her feelings in words. How could she describe the best day of her life? How could she describe the morning that she had spent talking with the boy on the island? She was sure that if she wrote down all the things they had said, the words would look stupid. And it would be difficult to describe the excitement she had felt when her 'friend' (what an amazing word!) had finally told her his name. It was strange, she thought. Most people tell you their name when you first meet them or when someone introduces you to them. But when the boy from the barn had finally told her his name, she felt as if he was sharing the biggest secret in the world. His name was John. She said the name aloud. Then she typed the name again and again. She had a friend and his name was John.

 www.macmillanenglish.com/owlhall

Kara had learnt that John was an only child – he had no brothers or sisters. Kara wondered how it would feel to be an only child and tried to imagine her life without Martin. Martin! She knew that Martin did not like John but things would be different if the two boys could spend some time together. She wondered what Martin had done all morning. Had he spent it in his room?

Kara decided she wanted to talk to Martin so she walked down the corridor and knocked on his door. But there was no answer. She knocked again.

'Martin?' she called. But there was only silence. Kara slowly turned the door handle and opened the door but Martin was not there. Then she realized that there was something different about the room. There were no sheets on the bed and there were no clothes on the floor. Where were Martin's things? What was happening? Was Martin playing one of his games?

'Martin?' Kara said. 'Where are you?'

But Martin did not answer.

Kara suddenly felt very alone. She went back to her room to see if Martin was there. But he was not.

'Kara!' her mother shouted from downstairs. 'Can you come down to the kitchen, please?'

Maybe Martin's already with Mum, Kara thought. She went quickly downstairs and into the kitchen. But the first thing she saw was Howard. He was standing next to the table with Max at his feet.

'Hello, Kara,' Howard said. Then he smiled at her and showed his perfect teeth.

Kara looked quickly around the room but Martin was not there. Then she looked at Mum.

'Mum?' Kara said. 'Have you seen Martin?'

Mum looked at Howard and Kara recognized her expression. It was the same look that she used to give Dad. It was the look that said, 'Talk to your daughter. Be a father.'

'What's happening?' Kara asked.

Howard sat down at the table. 'Your mother says that you've been sleepwalking,' he said to Kara.

Kara began to feel very angry. 'That's none of your business[P]! You're not my dad!' she shouted.

Mum put down the cups she was taking from a cupboard. 'Kara, please don't talk to Howard like that,' she said angrily. 'He's trying to help you.'

'If Howard wants to help me, then he can tell me where Martin is!' Kara said.

'Please don't start!' Mum said. 'Not about Martin, please!'

Howard looked at Kara. 'Please sit down,' he said in a voice full of authority[80]. 'We have to talk.'

Kara slowly sat down at the table.

'Martin is in a safe place,' Howard went on. 'You don't have to worry about him. You have to look after[81] yourself now. Your mother and I are worried about you and we want to help you.'

But Kara was not listening to Howard. She was worrying about Martin. What 'safe place'? What had Martin done? Where had they taken him? 'I promised not to leave him,' she cried.

'Please, Kara …' Mum said. 'Please don't start talking about Martin again.'

Kara turned to stare at Howard. 'Where is he?' she asked.

'I told you,' Howard said. 'Martin is in a safe place.'

'No!' Kara shouted. Then she got up and ran out of the kitchen. She started running up the stairs but then changed her mind[P].

There was something strange about Howard. She heard his words in her mind. 'Martin is *in a safe place*.' Where had he taken Martin? The only 'safe' place Kara could think of was Howard's house on the hill. Was Martin a prisoner there?

Kara ran back down the stairs and out through the front door. It was still light outside but the air felt cooler as she ran across the courtyard. She came to the bumpy track and followed it up the hill towards Howard's house. She did not know what she was going to do when she got to the house. She only knew that she had to find Martin.

The daylight was starting to go by the time Kara got to the house on the hill. She stood outside looking up at the dark windows. There were no lights on and she could not see anyone. But she thought she could hear voices coming from inside. She looked around to check that no one was watching her then she walked up to the front door. It was not locked so she opened it quietly and walked into the hall.

Kara's eyes slowly get used to[82] the darkness inside the house. She was standing in a long narrow hall. There was a table by the front door with some unopened letters on it. Kara picked one up. It was addressed to 'Doctor Howard Ward'.

Howard was a *doctor* …

Then she heard the voices again. At first she thought they were coming from one of the rooms but then she realized that they were coming from under the floor. Kara tried not to make any noise as she walked down the hall and past the staircase. She was feeling very frightened but she knew she had to find Martin. Behind the staircase there were some steps going down to another door. That must be the basement[83], Kara thought. Martin must be in the basement. Her heart started beating[84] faster as she turned the door handle. But the door was locked.

Kara looked around the hall for a key but she could not find one. What should she do? Should she shout his name? No. There were other people there. She could hear them talking.

If Martin was there too, they might hurt him. But why would they want to hurt her brother? For a moment Kara thought of calling the police. But then she had a better idea.

10

An Important Discovery

K ara knocked on the door of the small cottage and waited. A few seconds later a man opened the door and stared at her. He did not look very friendly.

'Is John here?' Kara asked.

Then John appeared behind the man. 'It's alright, Father,' John said. 'She's looking for me.'

'I suppose you want to come in,' the man said to Kara.

Kara thanked him and walked into the cottage. It was strange being inside it. She had passed it so many times since she had been at Owl Hall. It was much smaller than the main house and it felt cold inside. She followed John to his room.

'I need your help,' Kara said.

'What are you talking about?' John asked. 'What's happened?'

Kara stood by the door, feeling awkward.

'I think Martin has been kidnapped[85],' she said. 'I think Howard has taken him and locked him in the basement of his house. There are people inside and I can't open the door and I promised I wouldn't leave him. Please help me.'

John thought for a moment. Then he opened a drawer and took out a torch[86]. 'OK, Kara. Let's go and find him!' he said.

But Kara did not move. She was looking at the picture on the wall of John's room.

'What's that?' Kara asked.

John looked at the picture and laughed. 'It's a map of Treasure Island,' he said. 'It used to be my favourite book. I like islands. You know that.'

'And what's your favourite colour?' Kara asked.

'It's green,' he said. 'Why?'

Kara looked at the room's green walls. John's room was painted in his favourite colour and there was a picture from his favourite book on the wall. In the main house Kara's room was painted in her favourite colour and there was a copy of her favourite painting on the wall. Kara's head started going round in circles. What was happening to her?

'Come on!' John said, opening the door. His father was in the living room reading a very large book. He looked up as they walked past.

'Don't be too late,' his father said as they left the cottage. 'I have to get up early to work tomorrow.'

'I promise I won't be late, sir,' John said.

Then John followed Kara up the bumpy track to the house on the hill. They opened the front door and walked into the hall. Kara could still hear the voices from the basement but they were louder now and suddenly she recognized them.

'It's Mum!' Kara whispered. 'It's Mum and Howard's voices. What is Mum doing in the basement?'

John tried opening the basement door but it was still locked. Then he shone the torch on some shelves behind them. He lifted up a key from underneath a silver bowl.

'How did you know the key was there?' Kara asked.

'I'm a spy, remember?' John answered. 'Are you sure you want to do this?'

'Yes!' Kara said. 'Unlock the door!'

So John unlocked the door and opened it. The voices were louder now. Kara could hear that Mum was upset and Howard was trying to calm her down.

'You have to be patient, Janet,' Howard was saying.

'I can't be patient!' Mum cried. 'It happened more than six months ago. I can't do this anymore. I want Martin out of our lives!'

Kara followed John down the steps. There was a strange light coming from the basement and when they reached the bottom of the steps Kara could see that it was coming from a line of TV monitors[87] on a long desk. It looked like the control room of a television studio. There were different pictures on the screens but they were not from TV shows. They were from video cameras around Owl Hall. On each monitor there was an image of a different part of Owl Hall. And underneath each monitor there were labels which read: 'Entrance', 'Courtyard', 'East Cottage', 'West Cottage', 'Main House Kitchen'. Kara paused. Something was moving in the 'Main House Kitchen' picture. Kara moved closer until she could see Mum and Howard standing together in the Owl Hall kitchen. She could hear them talking too.

'You told me that everything would be alright!' Mum shouted at Howard.

'It *is* alright,' Howard replied. 'You heard what Kara said. She said that Martin had gone.'

'We have to find her,' her mother replied. Then she suddenly left the room, followed by Howard. A few seconds later they both appeared on one of the other monitors – they were walking across the courtyard, past the camera hidden in the silver sphere in the pond.

'Come with me,' Howard said. 'I know how we can find her.'

John took hold of Kara's hand. 'We have to leave,' he said. 'I think they're coming here.'

Kara's eyes were moving from monitor to monitor, she was trying to understand what she was seeing. Then she followed John back up the stairs.

He locked the basement door and left the key under the same bowl. Then they walked quickly out of the house and ran through the trees until they reached the barn.

'Let's hide in here,' John said. So they entered the barn and John sat down in the blue armchair.

'They won't find us here,' John said. 'There aren't any cameras in the barn.'

'But where's Martin?' Kara said. 'I thought he would be in the basement. I have to find him.'

'Kara, Martin's gone,' John said.

'What do you mean?' Kara replied.

'I mean you don't have to worry about Martin anymore,' John said. 'You can live your own life now.'

Kara sat down on the ground and put her head in her arms. 'You don't know anything about my brother,' she said.

'You're right,' John said. 'So tell me about 'the incident'.

51

What really happened six months ago? Tell me and then maybe I'll understand him better. Go on. What are you waiting for, Kara?'

Kara had not spoken about the incident to anyone. She had not even spoken to her mother about it or to her father. She had not spoken to the police or to the doctors. She had not even spoken to Martin. And now, here she was, in the middle of the countryside, sitting in an old barn with her only friend in the whole world. And for the first time she wanted to speak about it.

'OK,' she said. 'I'll tell you. But you must promise not to tell Mum or Howard.'

'I promise,' John said.

So Kara closed her eyes and started telling her story.

11

Kara's Story

'I don't know where to start ...' she said. 'But I suppose it was over six months ago on that Saturday morning when Mum and Dad told us that they were going to separate. They pretended that it was because of work. "Dad has to go to Australia as part of his new job," Mum told me. But I knew – Martin knew – we both knew the real reason he was going to Australia. We had both heard Mum and Dad arguing and shouting at each other. And we had heard the long silences when they hadn't spoken to each other. I'm not sure which was worse – the noise of the arguing or the silence. And while they were arguing or sitting in silence, we both felt like we weren't in the room. Sometimes Mum would say, "Let's talk about this later," or "Not in front of the kids". But most of the time they fought their war around us while we watched and said nothing. It made me unhappy of course, but Martin was younger and he didn't understand what was happening. He slowly became very quiet and very angry.

'On that Saturday, I was sitting in the living room with Martin while Mum and Dad were shouting at each other in the kitchen. Suddenly I saw Martin take a box of matches from the shelf and I knew that he was going to do something bad. I didn't try to stop him. He lit one of the matches and moved towards the waste-paper basket. He carefully lit the paper that was in the basket and watched the flames rise. Then he came and stood next to me. The smell of burning was strong and Mum and Dad came running in quickly. They just stood there. I remember the look of shock in Dad's eyes.

'I put the fire out. Then Martin started crying and I started shouting at Mum and Dad, telling them to stop arguing because it was making Martin angry. They spent the rest of the day being nice to us, telling us how much they loved us.

'Martin liked Mum and Dad being nice to him so, a few days later, he started burning some clothes in my bedroom.

'I suppose he thought that he could stop them from separating. He thought that if he kept lighting fires they would realize how bad he felt and maybe they would stay together. But they didn't. Dad even talked about separating *us*. "Maybe Martin could come and live with me in Australia and Kara could stay here with you," Dad said. But Mum wanted us to stay together. So Dad left and Martin became more upset and more angry.

'A few days after Dad had gone, I came home and found Martin in his room playing with a cigarette lighter. It was during the school holidays and Mum was out at work. We were the only ones in the house. I started shouting at Martin and I told him that he had to stop. I told him that Dad was never going to come home again. Martin said I was lying and that it was all my fault. It was my fault that Mum and Dad had argued. It was my fault that Dad had left home. That's when I said … I said …

'"Martin, I wish you were dead!"

'I didn't mean it. I was angry. Martin stared at me and I'll never forget the look in his eyes. He looked as if he hated me. Then he walked out of the room. I heard him leave the house, shutting the front door hard behind him. A few minutes later I went to find him. I felt bad about what I had said and I wanted to make things better again because I loved him. He was my little brother.

'I walked to the end of the street but I couldn't see him. I walked across the park near our house but he wasn't there. I looked everywhere but I couldn't find him. I sat down on a bench[88] and felt terrible. That was when I heard the sirens[89] and saw two – maybe three – fire engines driving past very fast. I knew immediately that something had happened and that Martin was responsible. So I ran after the fire engines and saw them disappear round the corner into our street.

'I ran as fast as I could and all the time I was thinking, *It's my fault*. I told Martin that I wished he was dead. I'm guilty.

'When I got to our street, there were people everywhere. The fire engines were in the middle of the street and the fire fighters were breaking down the front door to our house, trying to get inside the burning building. Our home was on fire and there was nothing they could do to stop it. Forty minutes later the house was just four walls with an empty black hole inside.

'So … that was the famous 'incident'. It was in all the newspapers and on TV. You probably saw it. I can still see the newspaper headlines – "Pyro Boy Burns Down Broken Home". I had to look the word up in the dictionary: "*Pyromaniac* – someone who wants to start fires because they have a mental illness[90]". It's an ugly word. An ugly word to describe people who do terrible things.'

John looked into Kara's eyes.

'And what happened to Martin?' he asked. 'Did the police find him?'

'I was the one who the police interviewed,' Kara replied. 'I was the one who had to see all the doctors and listen to all their questions. Nobody talked to Martin.'

'Why not?' John asked.

'Because …' Then Kara went silent.

'Because *what*?' John continued. He knelt down in front of Kara and held her hands. 'Let him go, Kara,' he said. 'Let him go.'

'What do you mean?' Kara asked.

'You heard his voice. You heard it when you arrived at Owl Hall, remember?' John said.

Kara remembered the voice that had whispered to her the night she arrived at Owl Hall. 'Kara!' it had said. 'Help me. Let me go!'

'Stop pretending,' John said.

'I'm not pretending,' Kara said.

'Then tell me what *really* happened to Martin,' John said.

There was a long silence and Kara could hear her heart beating. She wondered if John could hear it too. Then she looked into John's eyes and said the words for the first time.

'Martin is dead.'

The two of them looked at each other without speaking for a few seconds. Then John said, 'How did he die?'

Kara stared down at the ground. Then she slowly started to cry. 'When we argued, I heard the front door shut. I thought he'd left the house. But he hadn't. He stayed in the house and started the fire. But this time, I wasn't there to put it out. He died in the fire. Martin's dead.'

Kara suddenly felt as if a huge weight[91] had been lifted from her shoulders. Martin was dead. For the first time in six months she had said the words. 'Martin is dead.'

'So why have you been pretending that he's still alive?' John asked.

'Everybody thinks it was my fault,' Kara said.

'No, they don't,' John replied. 'Martin started the fire, not you. Everybody knows that.'

Kara's expression suddenly changed. She took her hands away from John and stood up. She looked at John like she was looking at a stranger.

'How do you know?' she asked. 'How do you know what everybody thinks?'

'I –' John started to answer but Kara stopped him.

'You knew, didn't you? All this time, you knew that Martin was dead! Why didn't you say anything?' she asked.

'I wanted to help you,' John said.

'You work for the doctor, don't you?' she said. 'You work for Howard. That's why you became my friend. You're not really my friend, are you? This was all a trick!'

'No, Kara,' John said.

But Kara was not listening. She felt the tears running down her face and she turned and ran from the barn. She wanted to escape everything and everyone so she ran as fast as she could back to the main house. As she came into the courtyard, Mum and Howard appeared at the front door. Mum looked frightened.

'Kara!' she shouted. 'Where have you been? We've been looking for you everywhere. Oh darling, are you alright?'

'Stop lying to me!' Kara said. 'Everybody's lying to me. Tell me the truth. I want to know the truth!'

12

A New Beginning

Kara, Mum and Howard sat at the kitchen table. Mum had made a pot of tea. She poured the tea nervously and looked at Howard. Howard understood and started speaking.

'Kara,' he said. 'Your mother contacted me because she thought I might be able to help you.'

'One of your other doctors told me about Owl Hall, Kara,' said Mum. 'It has a fantastic reputation[92].'

'A reputation for *what?*' Kara asked.

'Owl Hall is one of the best CTTs in the country,' Howard continued.

'CTT?' asked Kara.

'Centre for Troubled Teenagers,' he said. 'We provide a space for families to sort out difficulties. If parents are having problems with their teenage children then they can come and spend some time here together. Being at Owl Hall is like being on holiday so we can watch the relationships between parents and children. Then we suggest ways of improving things. We also encourage our guests to write a blog so we can understand what they are thinking.'

'*You've* read my blog?' Kara asked.

'As your doctor, yes. I can promise you that everything is private,' Howard said. 'No one else has read your blog, not even your mother.'

'You're *not* my doctor,' Kara said.

'Don't be angry, darling,' Mum said. 'You needed help. We both needed help.'

'It wasn't my fault,' Kara said before she could stop herself. 'Martin's death … the fire …'

There was a pause while Mum looked at Howard and Howard looked at Kara.

Then Mum looked back at Kara. 'Of course it wasn't your fault,' Mum said slowly. 'It was my fault and your father's fault, but it was never your fault. All this time I thought you were trying to keep Martin alive as a way to punish[93] me. Howard has helped me understand what was really happening. I didn't know that you felt guilty too.'

There was an awkward silence.

Then Howard said, 'The main thing is that you're both getting better now, Kara – you and your mother.'

'Yes. Thanks to you, Howard,' Mum said.

'Why are you thanking Howard?' Kara said. 'He didn't do anything. You should thank John.'

'Who's John?' Mum asked.

'He's Howard's assistant,' Kara replied.

When Howard heard this he looked confused.

'You never told me about an assistant,' Mum said to Howard.

'I don't have an assistant,' Howard said.

Kara thought about Howard's words for a moment. Was he telling the truth?

'Then who is John? Is he another patient?' Kara asked. 'Are all the people I've seen at Owl Hall your patients?'

Howard looked at Kara for a long time. Then he shook his head. 'I'm sorry, but I can't discuss other patients at Owl Hall,' he said.

Suddenly Kara's mother wanted to know more about John. Who was he? How old was he? How long had Kara known him? Kara did not want to answer Mum's questions so she got up quickly and walked out of the kitchen. She needed to find John.

The moon was bright and Kara ran back to the barn but he was not there. She went to John's cottage and knocked on the door but it was John's father who opened it.

'Is John here?' she asked.

'No,' replied his father impatiently. 'He hasn't come back yet. Now, if you'll excuse me … I'm very busy working.'

Kara ran on. She ran up the bumpy track to Howard's house on the hill. Inside, she ran straight to the door to the basement but it was still locked. So she took the key from under the silver bowl, unlocked the door and went down the stairs. But John was not there. She looked at all the monitors with their pictures of Owl Hall. She was hoping to see John on one of them but he did not appear.

Then she saw something on the desk in the basement. It was a large blue folder, full of papers. Someone had written something on the front of the folder – 'Case #X450899'.

Kara looked inside the folder and found a large photograph of herself. There were newspaper cuttings about 'the incident' in the folder. There were school reports and reports from the police and the other doctors she had seen. There were copies of all her blog entries and a form on which Howard had made a note of everything Kara had done since she had arrived at

Owl Hall. At the bottom of the form Howard had written in big letters 'See Case #X450892'.

Kara looked around her. In the corner of the room there was a filing cabinet[94]. She opened the top drawer and saw that it was full of folders. They were all different colours and had different case numbers on the covers. Kara searched for case #X450892 and found it almost immediately. She opened the folder and found herself looking at a photograph of John. The folder was full of papers and she wondered what they were. Were they police reports? Newspaper stories? Then Kara saw something else in the folder.

It was a map … of an island.

———

'John!' Kara shouted.

John was sitting alone on his island, writing in his red book. But when he heard Kara's voice, he stood up.

'I need to see you!' she cried.

Kara was standing at the side of the lake and waving to John. John quickly got into the boat and a few minutes later he was standing next to Kara. John smiled nervously.

'So we're still friends?' he asked.

'Yes … We're still friends,' Kara answered.

'You're crazy,' he said.

'That's what the doctors say,' Kara said. They both laughed and then they looked at each other for a long time.

'Do you ever want to be someone else?' John asked.

'I don't know,' Kara replied. 'Sometimes, I guess.'

'I do,' said John. 'All the time.'

'Why?' Kara said. 'I don't want you to be anyone else. I think you're really clever. You know more about me than I do. And you knew about this place.'

'The island?' asked John.

'No. Owl Hall, stupid,' said Kara.

They both laughed again.

'You don't need to be clever to know what's going on here,' John said. 'How many holiday homes do you know with so many cameras? I knew there was something wrong with this place as soon as I arrived.'

'You *should* be a spy,' Kara said.

'I know,' he said. 'It didn't take me long to find the basement and the key to get inside. I spent a lot of time in there. And no one ever found me. I could always see when Howard was coming back by looking at the monitors.'

'That's how you knew so much about my past and about Martin. You read my case file,' said Kara.

'And I hacked[95] into the computer system so I could send you messages,' said John. 'Howard never discovered them.'

'What about your dad?' Kara asked. 'What did he think you were doing?'

'I don't know,' John said. 'He doesn't care about me.'

'Of course he does. Why do you call him *sir?*' Kara asked.

'He thinks children should always obey their parents,' said John. 'We've never been close. Not like you and your mum. You're lucky. My dad's always busy with his work.'

Then John looked away from Kara. 'So do you know my story now?' he asked. 'Did you read my case file? About what happened at school?'

'No, I didn't,' Kara replied. 'But when you're ready, you can tell me about it. I want to hear your story from you and not from some notes or reports.'

Then Kara looked at the red book that John was holding. 'What are you writing?' she asked.

'Words,' John said.

'You love words, don't you?' said Kara.

John did not answer.

'You should be a writer,' Kara said.

The boy moved nervously. 'I don't think so,' he said. 'Words are dangerous.'

'Dangerous?' Kara said. 'How are they dangerous?'

'Words can hurt,' replied John. 'Sometimes words can kill.'

John looked very unhappy and Kara knew he was thinking about something from another time and place. Kara did not ask him any more questions.

———

The next morning, Kara wrote her final blog entry. It was the craziest blog entry she had ever written. She knew that Howard would read it and she wanted to give him something special to read.

www.macmillanenglish.com/owlhall

Then, after breakfast, Mum told Kara to pack her things. They were leaving Owl Hall and going home.

They had moved into their new home four months ago. It was in a new town and Kara had thought she would never make any friends. But now she had a friend and the future looked brighter. Kara was happy to go home but sad to leave John. He had helped her and now she wanted to help him.

Howard came to say goodbye to them. He seemed sad to see them leaving. Even Max looked sad.

'Don't you want to say goodbye to your friend?' Mum asked.

Kara shook her head. John was a good spy and Kara was sure that he knew what was happening. He was probably sitting in the control room now, watching them all on one of the monitors. If John wanted to say goodbye then he would come and find her. She secretly hoped he would.

Mum and Kara put their cases in the back of the car. As she was getting into the car, Kara thought she heard a voice whispering to her.

'Kara. I'm sorry,' the voice said.

She looked up and saw Martin standing at one of the bedroom windows. Kara knew that it wasn't really Martin but he looked so real.

*She looked up and saw Martin standing at
one of the bedroom windows.*

'Thanks for letting me go,' Martin whispered. 'I'm free now.'

For a moment Kara felt sad as she remembered her dead brother. Then Mum waved goodbye to Howard and started the engine. She drove the car out through the gate of Owl Hall and down the track towards the road. Kara looked back. She thought she could still see Martin at the window. Then suddenly Mum put her foot on the brake and the car stopped.

Kara turned round and saw John in front of them. He was standing in the middle of the track. Then he walked round to her side of the car and Kara opened the window.

'Hi,' John said.

'Hi,' Kara said.

Kara turned to Mum. 'Mum?' she said. 'This is my friend. His name is John.' Then she turned to John. 'This is my mum.'

'Hello,' John said.

'Nice to meet you,' Mum said to John. 'You must come and visit us soon. Kara would like that, wouldn't you, Kara?'

Kara nodded her head. John was holding a package. It was about the size of a box of chocolates, wrapped in brown paper with a string tied around it.

'This is for you,' John said. Then he held out the parcel and Kara took it.

'Thanks,' she said.

John stepped back and Kara's mother started driving slowly away.

'Chapter Thirteen is the best part!' John called.

Kara watched him grow smaller and smaller as her mother drove away. Then the car turned the corner and they were back on the main road.

'He seems like a nice boy,' Mum said.

Kara untied the string and opened the parcel. Inside she found the red book that John had been writing in. She opened the book and read 'To Kara' on the first page. Then she turned the page and started reading:

Chapter One

Arrival

*Kara leant her head against the car window and looked out at the
other cars driving past on the motorway. Where had the cars been?
Where were they going? Who were the people sitting inside them and
what were they thinking?*

Kara smiled. John had written the story of her visit to Owl
Hall. She turned the pages and read sentences that told the
story of her past few days. There were the funny moments, sad
moments and the frightening moments. Then she remembered
John's last words: 'Chapter Thirteen is the best part!'

Kara quickly looked through the book. She reached the
end of Chapter Twelve and then turned the page.

Chapter Thirteen

Points for Understanding

1

1 What time of day was it at the start of the story?
2 Who is Martin?
3 Where did Kara think they were going?
4 Why could Mum not use her mobile phone to find their location?
5 How did Kara feel about Howard when she first saw him?
6 What happened to the road sign?

2

1 Did Kara like Owl Hall when she first saw it?
2 What did Kara notice in the courtyard?
3 How many holiday homes were there at Owl Hall?
4 What was on the wall of Kara's room?
5 Could Kara log on to the Internet on the laptop?
6 Why was Martin nervous at the end of the chapter?

3

1 Kara said to Mum, 'Are you worried I'm going to do something stupid again?' What do you think Kara meant?
2 What was Martin doing when Kara walked into the living room?
3 Did Mum want to talk about 'the incident' at breakfast?
4 What did Kara use to film the video?
5 What did Kara think she saw when she filmed the barn?

4

1 When did Martin's character start to change?
2 Who did Kara and Martin think lived in the house on the hill?
3 What did they see when they watched the video?
4 Why did Mum ask Kara to make some tea?

5

1 What did the colours in the van Gogh painting make Kara think of?
2 Why did Kara tell Martin that he could not go with her to the barn?
3 Why was Kara surprised when she saw the inside of the barn?
4 Why did Kara wonder if her mother had met Howard before?
5 What did Martin want to do after supper?
6 How did Kara stop Martin from finding the spy?

6

1 What was Kara looking at when she first saw the boy?
2 Why did the boy like the barn?
3 Did Kara tell the boy what the voice said when she arrived at Owl Hall? Why? / Why not?
4 On the stairs, Martin said, 'Last night you lied to me, Kara.' What did he mean?
5 Why did Kara stay with Martin for the rest of the day?

7

1 What did Kara hear in the middle of the night?
2 Where did she follow the noise to?
3 What was Martin doing when Kara found him?
4 Why did he run into the building?
5 Was Owl Hall really on fire?
6 Why was Kara confused when she talked to Martin in his room?

8

1 In what ways were Kara and Martin different?
2 What was the boy doing when Kara found him in the barn?
3 Where was Martin?
4 What did Kara see from the top of the hill on the other side of the wood?
5 What was near the other side of the lake?
6 How did they get there?
7 Why did the boy think they were both at Owl Hall?

9

1   What did Kara do as soon as she got back to the house?
2   What was strange about Martin's room when Kara went in?
3   Where did Howard say Martin was?
4   Where did Kara go to look for Martin?
5   What did Kara learn about Howard in his house?
6   What did Kara hear in the house?
7   What idea do you think Kara had at the end of the chapter?

10

1   What was strange about John's room?
2   What did Kara and John find in the basement of Howard's house?
3   Who said, 'I want Martin out of our lives'?
4   Why did John think the barn was a safe place to hide?
5   When did 'the incident' happen?

11

1   What did Mum and Dad tell Kara and Martin six months ago?
2   Why did Martin keep lighting fires?
3   Who did Martin say was responsible for the problems at home?
4   What happened to Martin?
5   What did Kara suddenly think was the real reason John became her friend?

12

1   Why did the doctor encourage his patients to keep a blog?
2   Did Mum think 'the incident' was Kara's fault?
3   If John does not work for the doctor, who is he?
4   How did John find out about Kara's story?
5   When Kara first arrived at Owl Hall she heard a voice whisper, 'Kara! Help me. Let me go!' Whose voice was it?
6   When John gave Kara the book, why do you think he said, 'Chapter Thirteen is the best part'?

Glossary

1 **yawning** – to yawn (page 6)
to open your mouth wide and take a big breath because you are tired or bored

2 **imagined** – to imagine something (page 7)
to form a picture of someone or something in your mind

3 **realized** – to realize something (page 7)
to gradually begin to understand something that you did not know or notice before

4 **caravan** (page 7)
a vehicle that people can live and travel in on holiday

5 **expression** (page 7)
a look on someone's face that shows what their thoughts or feelings are

6 **signal** (page 7)
when you are close enough to an electrical signal, it means you can make and receive calls on your mobile phone. When there is no signal, your mobile phone does not work.

7 **kicked** – to kick something (page 7)
to hit someone or something with your foot

8 **narrow** (page 7)
if something is narrow, there is only a short distance from one side of it to the other

9 **lit up** – to light up something (page 7)
to make something brighter by pointing light at it or to make somewhere brighter by giving it light

10 **crossroads** (page 8)
a place where one road crosses another

11 **handle** (page 8)
the part of something that you use for opening or holding it

12 **growling** – to growl (page 8)
if an animal growls, it makes a low, frightening noise

13 **staring** – to stare at someone or something (page 8)
to look directly at someone or something for a long time

14 **flashing** – to flash (page 8)
to shine on and off very quickly or to make a light do this

15 **collar** (page 8)
a thin piece of leather or plastic that a dog or cat wears around its neck

16 **hurt** – *to hurt someone* (page 9)
   to cause someone physical pain or injury
17 **bumpy** (page 9)
   a bumpy road has a rough surface and is uncomfortable to travel on
18 **track** (page 9)
   a path or road with a rough surface
19 **bush** (page 10)
   a plant that is smaller than a tree and has a lot of thin branches
20 **creaked** – *to creak* (page 10)
   if something creaks, it makes a noise when it moves or when you
   put weight on it. A creak can be a low sound or it can be high like
   a squeak.
21 **waved** – *to wave* (page 10)
   to move your hand in order to tell someone to move
22 **driveway** (page 10)
   a wide path for cars that leads from a road to someone's house
23 **exploring** – *to explore* (page 11)
   to travel or walk around an area in order to learn about it
24 **surrounded** – *to surround something* (page 11)
   to be all around something or someone
25 **courtyard** (page 11)
   a square area outside that is surrounded by buildings or walls
26 **security** (page 11)
   safety from attack, harm or damage. A *security light* and a *security
   camera* are electrical devices which help provide safety and
   protection because they allow people to see what is happening
   somewhere.
27 **pond** (page 11)
   a small area of water, usually in a garden
28 **sphere** (page 11)
   an object that is round like a ball
29 **spooky** (page 11)
   strange and frightening
30 **Welcome Pack** (page 11)
   a set of documents that is given to visitors so that they have all the
   information they need about the place they are visiting
31 **cottage** (page 12)
   a small house usually in a village or in the countryside
32 **lake** (page 12)
   a large area of water surrounded by land

33 *corridor* (page 12)
a long passage inside a building with doors on each side

34 *prison cell* (page 13)
a small room where a prisoner – someone who has committed a crime – is kept

35 *cut off – to be cut off from someone or something* (page 13)
to be unable to leave a place or communicate with other people who are not in the same place

36 *click – to click (on something)* (page 13)
to make a computer do something by pressing a button on the mouse

37 *log on – to log on* (page 13)
to start using a computer system. When you stop using a computer system, you *log out.*

38 *fingernails* (page 14)
the hard, smooth parts at the ends of your fingers

39 *awkward* (page 15)
not comfortable, relaxed or confident

40 *privacy* (page 15)
the freedom to do things without other people watching you or knowing what you are doing

41 *kneeling down – to kneel down* (page 16)
to put or have your knee or both knees on the ground

42 *match* (page 16)
a small stick that produces a flame when it is rubbed against a rough surface

43 *rushed – to rush somewhere* (page 17)
to move somewhere very quickly

44 *incident* (page 17)
something that happens and which is often unusual, violent or dangerous

45 *alone* (page 18)
if you are alone, no one else is with you

46 *solution* (page 18)
a way to solve a problem or deal with a bad situation

47 *barn* (page 19)
a large building on a farm where animals, crops or machines are kept

48 *figure* (page 19)
the shape of a person which you see in the distance

49 **spy** (page 21)
someone who watches someone secretly and tries to discover
information about them
50 **stick** (page 21)
a piece of wood, often a thin piece and especially one that has been
broken or cut from a tree
51 **ginger** (page 21)
ginger hair or fur is an orange-brown colour
52 **slim** (page 21)
thin in an attractive way
53 **well-built** (page 21)
a well-built person has a strong, attractive body
54 **outgoing** (page 21)
someone who is outgoing is friendly and enjoys meeting and talking
to people
55 **separate** – *to separate* (page 21)
to stop living with your husband, wife or partner
56 **stroked** – *to stroke something* (page 22)
to gently move your hand over skin, hair or fur
57 **wagged** – *to wag something* (page 22)
if a dog wags its tail, it moves its tail from one side to the other
several times
58 **trap** (page 23)
a trick that is designed to catch someone or make them do
something that they did not mean to do
59 **utility room** (page 24)
a small room that contains equipment such as a washing machine
and tumble dryer
60 **treadmill** (page 24)
a piece of exercise equipment with a moving surface that you walk
or run on
61 **curious** (page 27)
wanting to find out about something
62 **attracted** – *to be attracted to someone* (page 27)
to be interested in someone in a romantic way
63 **dart** (page 27)
a small pointed object that you throw at a round board called a
dartboard in a game called *darts*. When you play darts, you try to hit
the circle in the centre of the dartboard. The centre is called the
bullseye.

64 **pool** (page 27)
   a game in which two players hit balls into holes or pockets round the edge of a table using a long stick called a *cue*

65 **hunting** – *to hunt someone or something* (page 27)
   to try to find someone or something

66 **warning** (page 29)
   something that you say to tell someone about a possible problem or danger so that they can avoid it or deal with it. When you give someone a warning, you *warn* them.

67 **reflection** (page 30)
   an image that you see when you look in a mirror or at a shiny surface

68 **embarrassed** (page 32)
   feeling slightly ashamed and worried about what other people will think of you

69 **investigate** – *to investigate* (page 36)
   to try to find out all the facts about something in order to learn the truth about it

70 **shone** – *to shine* (page 36)
   when a light shines on something, it lights it up and makes it bright. If you *shine something on something*, you direct the light from a source such as a torch onto something to make it bright.

71 **pouring** – *to pour* (page 36)
   to flow continuously and in large amounts

72 **collapsed** – *to collapse* (page 37)
   if a building or other structure collapses, it falls down

73 **sleepwalking** – *to sleepwalk* (page 37)
   to walk and sometimes do other things while you are still sleeping

74 **neat** (page 40)
   things that are neat look nice because they have been arranged carefully

75 **stream** (page 41)
   a small, narrow river

76 **rowing boat** (page 42)
   a small boat that you move by pulling on two poles with flat ends called *oars*. If you move a boat in this way, you *row*.

77 **upside down** (page 42)
   with the top part at the bottom and the bottom part at the top

78 **bounce** – *to bounce* (page 44)
if an object *bounces*, it hits a surface then immediately moves away. It can do this several times, with the *bounces* getting smaller and smaller each time.
79 **sank** – *to sink* (page 44)
to disappear below the surface of the water
80 **authority** (page 46)
the power to make decisions and make people do what you want
81 **look after** – *to look after someone or something* (page 46)
to take care of someone or something
82 **used to** (page 47)
familiar with something because you have experienced it before, so that it no longer seems difficult or strange
83 **basement** (page 47)
the part of a building below the level of the ground
84 **beating** – *to beat* (page 47)
if someone's heart beats, it makes regular movements and sounds
85 **kidnapped** – *to kidnap someone* (page 48)
to take someone away illegally and make them a prisoner, especially in order to make their family or a government give you money to get them back
86 **torch** (page 48)
a small electric light that you hold in your hand
87 **monitor** (page 50)
a screen that shows pictures or information
88 **bench** (page 54)
a hard seat for two or more people to sit on outside
89 **siren** (page 54)
a piece of equipment that makes a loud sound in order to warn people
90 **mental illness** (page 54)
an illness that affects someone's mind
91 **weight** (page 56)
a heavy object that is difficult to lift or move
92 **reputation** (page 57)
the opinion people have about how good or bad someone or something is
93 **punish** – *to punish someone* (page 58)
to do something unpleasant to someone because they have done something bad or illegal

94 **filing cabinet** (page 60)
   a tall piece of furniture with drawers in which you keep documents
95 **hacked** – *to hack into something* (page 61)
   to use a computer in order to connect secretly and illegally to
   someone else's computer

Useful Phrases

by the way (page 9)
used for adding a remark that is not relevant to the main subject of your conversation

just in time (page 19)
almost too late to do something

they came face to face – *to come face to face with someone* (page 22)
to meet someone suddenly, often when you are not expecting to meet them

there was something about – *there is something about someone or something* (page 32)
used for saying that someone or something has a particular quality but you are not certain what it is

Leave Kara alone – *to leave someone alone* (page 33)
used for telling someone to stop annoying or criticizing someone

broke your promise – *to break your promise* (page 34)
to not do something that you promised or agreed to do

kept her promise – *to keep your promise* (page 34)
to do what you said you would do

Keep out! (page 40)
used on signs to tell people not to go into a place

they had something in common – *to have something in common with someone* (page 41)
to have the same interests or opinions as someone else

none of your business – *to be none of your business* (page 46)
used for telling someone that you are not going to tell them about something because it does not affect or involve them

changed her mind – *to change your mind* (page 46)
to change a decision you have made or an opinion you have about something

Glossary and Useful Phrases definitions adapted from the Macmillan Essential Dictionary
© *Macmillan Publishers Limited 2003* www.macmillandictionary.com

Exercises

The Story

Choose the correct information to complete the sentences.

1 Kara was <u>excited</u> / (<u>not excited</u>) about the holiday.

2 They had <u>some problems</u> / <u>no problems</u> finding Owl Hall.

3 They arrived at Owl Hall in the <u>daytime</u> / <u>evening</u>.

4 Kara <u>liked</u> / <u>didn't like</u> the man who helped them.

5 Kara had a <u>good</u> / <u>bad</u> feeling about Owl Hall.

6 Martin's bedroom was <u>empty</u> / <u>comfortable</u>.

7 Kara <u>was able</u> / <u>wasn't able</u> to use the Internet.

8 Martin had <u>the same feeling as</u> / <u>a different feeling from</u> Kara about Owl Hall.

9 Martin wanted to <u>start</u> / <u>stop</u> a fire.

10 Kara used <u>a camera</u> / <u>her phone</u> to film Owl Hall.

11 While she was filming, Kara saw a strange <u>person</u> / <u>thing</u>.

12 When their parents separated, Kara <u>always</u> / <u>rarely</u> knew what Martin was thinking.

13 Kara received a message asking her to <u>email</u> / <u>meet</u> someone she didn't know.

14 Kara met John at <u>5.00 pm</u> / <u>8.00 am</u>.

15 Martin <u>liked</u> / <u>didn't like</u> John.

16 Martin thought Kara had <u>lied to him</u> / <u>told him the truth</u>.

People in the Story

Write a name from the box next to the correct information below.

> Howard   John   Kara   Kara's dad   Kara's mum   Martin

1 ....Howard.... was about forty.

2 .... had green eyes.

3 .... did not like talking about problems.

4 .... went to Australia.

5 .... was strong.

6 .... had brown hair.

7 .... had perfect teeth.

8 .... was tall.

9 .... had red hair.

10 .... thought it was important to talk about problems.

11 .... thought he was different.

12 .... had dark hair.

Multiple Choice

Tick the best answer.

1 During the night
  a there was a fire in the barn.
  b Kara dreamt there was a fire. ✓
  c there was a fire at Owl Hall.

2 The next morning, Kara
  a talked to Martin.
  b wrote a note to Martin.
  c met her new friend in the barn.

3 In the boat, Kara felt
  a worried about Martin.
  b she couldn't trust the boy.
  c calm and relaxed.

4 Back at Owl Hall, Kara thought that Howard
  a wanted to help her.
  b was a friendly man.
  c knew where Martin was.

5 In the basement of Howard's house, Kara found
  a TV monitors of Owl Hall.
  b her mother and Howard.
  c Martin.

6 Martin had started to light fires to
  a make Kara angry.
  b make his parents angry.
  c get his parents' attention.

7 In one of the fires,
  a Kara died.
  b their mother died.
  c Martin died.

8 Kara felt
  a it was her fault.
  b it was her mother's fault.
  c it was Martin's fault.

9 Owl Hall was
  a a holiday home.
  b a hospital.
  c a place where young people are helped with their problems.

10 John was
  a a ghost.
  b a patient.
  c a spy.

11 John gave Kara
  a a box of chocolates.
  b a book by his favourite writer.
  c a story he wrote about Kara and Owl Hall.

Words from the Story

Complete the gaps. Use each word in the box once.

attracted   authority   caravan   curious   cut off   expression   incident
investigate   ~~kidnapped~~   matches   outgoing   spooky   track   warned

1   Kara thought someone had _____*kidnapped*_____ Martin.

2   Owl Hall looked dark and frightening. It was _____ .

3   There was only a small road to Owl Hall. It was just a

    _____ .

4   Kara thought her mum wanted to stay in a _____ .

5   Mum looked different when the man said he was Howard. The
    _____ on her face changed.

6   Kara could not contact anyone by phone or email. She was

    _____ .

7   Kara wanted to know more about Howard. She was

    _____ .

8   She didn't think that Howard had the _____ to tell her
    what to do.

9   Kara _____ John about Martin. She told him that
    Martin was looking for him.

10   Kara wanted to find out what the noises were, so she decided to

     _____ .

11   Martin started fires with paper and used _____ to make
     the fire.

12   Kara thought that her mother was _____ to Howard
     and that she liked him.

13   Martin talked a lot and was more _____ than Kara.

14   Something bad had happened, which Kara called the

     _____ .

Vocabulary: Anagrams

Write the letters in the correct order to make words from the story.

1	PANIERTOUT	*reputation*	the opinion people have of you
2	CHORT		a light you can carry
3	ESCALLOP		to fall down
4	AMBERSREADS		feeling bad because you did something stupid
5	DREAMTILL		a machine you can run or walk on
6	RAPT		a plan to catch someone
7	SOLIUNTO		an answer to a problem
8	NESHI		to produce light like the sun
9	NARB		a building on a farm to keep animals or food from the land in
10	VARYPIC		being free to do what you want without other people knowing
11	TRASE		to look at a person or a thing for a long time
12	WANY		to open your mouth and breathe deeply because you are tired or bored
13	ELECTRONIF		the picture you see when you look in a mirror

Now complete the sentences with six of the words you have made.

1 Owl Hall's _____reputation_____ for helping young people was very good.

2 The fire caused the roof to _____ .

3 Kara's mother exercised on a _____ .

4 Kara first saw John in the _____ in the mirror.

5 Howard tried to find a _____ to Kara's problems.

6 John used a _____ so he could see where he was going.

Word Focus

Write the words in the box in the correct part of the table. Write three words in each part.

basement ~~click~~ collar corridor cottage growl hack into lake
log on monitor pond ~~sink~~ stream ~~stroke~~ ~~utility room~~ wag

Words connected to dogs	Words connected to buildings
stroke	utility room
Words connected to water	Words connected to technology
sink	click

83

Useful Phrases

Choose the correct words to make phrases from the story.

1 When the car stopped, Kara came (face) / nose to face with Max.

2 Kara looked up just <u>of / in</u> time to see a man in the bushes.

3 There was something <u>with / about</u> John that she liked.

4 Martin told John to leave Kara <u>alone / away</u>.

5 Kara broke her <u>promise / saying</u> when she left Martin alone.

6 Martin wanted Kara to keep her <u>words / promise</u>.

7 When Martin wanted to be alone he wrote a sign that said 'Keep <u>off / out</u>!'

8 Kara felt she had something in <u>understanding / common</u> with John.

9 She thought her life was none of Howard's <u>business / job</u>.

10 Kara changed her <u>memory / mind</u> about going back to Owl Hall.

Match sentences 1–10 above to sentences a–j below.

a She didn't do what she said she would do.   _5_

b She suddenly saw Max through the car window. ....

c He didn't want to speak to anyone. ....

d They both thought the same way. ....

e She almost didn't see him. ....

f She didn't think he should have any interest in her life. ....

g She decided to go somewhere else instead. ....

h He wanted her to do what she said she would do. ....

i He didn't want John to meet Kara anymore. ....

j She didn't know exactly what she liked about him, but she liked him.
....

Grammar: Relative pronouns

Join the sentences using *who*, *which* or *where*.

1 They saw a road. It went on for miles.
They saw a road which went on for miles.

2 There was a man. He had perfect teeth.

3 There was a sign. It said 'Owl Hall'.

4 There was a picture. It was painted by van Gogh.

5 There was a website. It had three links.

6 She went to the living room. Martin was making a fire there.

7 She opened the message. It was from a friend.

8 There was a barn. It was full of old things.

9 Kara had a terrible dream. It made her feel afraid.

10 John took her to a place. She felt calm and relaxed there.

11 She saw a boy in the window. He looked like Martin.

Grammar: Irregular past simple verbs

Complete the table with the past simple form of the verbs.

Infinitive	Past simple
1 see	*saw*
2 meet	
3 hear	
4 make	
5 find	
6 burn	
7 leave	
8 go	
9 give	

Grammar: Past simple and past continuous

Choose the correct form, in the past simple or past continuous, to complete the sentences.

1 Kara _____*saw*_____ (see) a man and woman arguing when she
   ____*was going*____ (go) to Owl Hall.

2 They _____ (look) for Owl Hall when they _____
   (meet) Howard.

3 Kara _____ (try) to open the car door when she
   _____ (see) a dog.

4 When she _____ (arrive) at Owl Hall Kara thought
   someone _____ (watch) her.

5 Kara _____ (hear) a voice when she _____ (close)
   the gate.

6 Martin and Kara .... (explore) the house when they
.... (find) a laptop.

7 Martin .... (make) a fire when Kara ....
(find) him.

8 Kara .... (film) Owl Hall when she .... (see)
a man in the bushes.

9 It .... (start) to rain when Kara .... (walk)
back to the house.

10 Kara .... (sleepwalk) when she .... (see)
Martin in a burning building.

11 Kara .... (discover) the TV monitors when she
.... (search) Howard's house with John.

12 Martin .... (start) a fire when his parents ....
(argue).

13 Kara .... (leave) Owl Hall when John ....
(give) her a present.

Grammar: Prepositions

Complete the sentences using the prepositions in the box.

~~about~~ across at into over to

1 Kara worried .... *about* .... Martin.

2 Kara's mum smiled .... Howard.

3 Kara talked .... John about Martin.

4 John and Kara climbed .... a gate.

5 John threw stones .... the water.

6 Kara and John jumped .... a stream.

Published by Macmillan Heinemann ELT
Between Towns Road, Oxford OX4 3PP
A division of Macmillan Publishers Limited
Companies and representatives throughout the world
Heinemann is the registered trademark of Pearson Education, used under licence.

ISBN 978–0–230–42281–0
ISBN 978–0–230–42283–4 (with CD edition)

First published 2012

Designed by Carolyn Gibson
Illustrated by Simon Williams
Cover photograph provided by Corbis/Tom Brakefield–The Stock Conne/
Science Fiction

Special thanks to Dr James Campbell and Joyce Campbell.

These materials may contain links for third party websites. We have no
control over, and are not responsible for, the contents of such third party
websites. Please use care when accessing them.

Although we have tried to trace and contact copyright holders before
publication, in some cases this has not been possible. If contacted we will be
pleased to rectify any errors or omissions at the earliest opportunity.

Printed and bound in Thailand

without CD edition

2017	2016	2015	2014	2013	2012
10	9	8	7	6	5	4	3	2

with CD edition

2017	2016	2015	2014	2013	2012
10	9	8	7	6	5	4	3	2